# ANIMAL KINGDOM

## A DIVERSITY FABLE

## WILLIAM A. GUILLORY, PH.D.

# Animal Kingdom

This is a work of fiction. Names, characters, places, and incidents are products of the author's imagination or are used fictionally and may or may not correspond to real situations. The depiction of events or situations relating to how nature, animals, or the ecosystem actually operates is not intended to be absolutely accurate for the sake of the story and its message. Any resemblance to actual events, locales, organizations, groups, or persons, living or dead, is entirely coincidental.

Animal Kingdom
Copyright © by William A. Guillory, Ph.D., March 2004

First Edition: 2005
LCCN: 2004107848
ISBN: 0-933241-23-2
Printed in the United States of America

Cover design by: Tatiana Haynes

Published by Innovations International, Inc.,
Publishing Division
310 East 4500 South, Suite #420
Salt Lake City, UT 84107 USA
(801) 268-3313 Tel
(801) 268-3422 Fax
Email: waguillory@qwest.net

 **A**nimal **K**ingdom

*To the one constant who*
*has been there for me*
*my entire life,*

*My sister Barbara.*

## Comments from Readers

*"Super read for all ages.* Couldn't put it down!"

"This book could be about nations, races, or cultures.
*I loved the story!"*

"The story draws the reader in wondering where you are
taking us — to a *powerful ending!"*

*"I am applying the principles in this book* to working
with people from around the world!"

*"This book is an in-depth approach* to how we should
function as a human race!"

*"Great book!!!* I absolutely loved it,
great parallels!"

*"This book is really good!* The ending is not
predictable from the start!

## Foreword

The purpose of a fable is to communicate a simple yet important message. In *Animal Kingdom*, the message is to learn to "see through the eyes of others as a necessity to compatibly live and work together in greater harmony." In this story, several diverse groups of animals must learn how to work together to survive an impending crisis. In order to do so, each group must first learn how to set aside their own opinions, ideas, and even values in order to achieve a compatible solution. Bill Guillory has skillfully used various animal groups to represent families, communities, cities, and nations who continually struggle to create harmony by reconciling differences.

I had the honor of being one of the first readers of *Animal Kingdom* while Bill was working on his early drafts. Shortly after reading the second draft, I was eating lunch with the production team at my company. We were discussing certain issues the production team was having with the sales team. The issues were beginning to build a wall between the two teams and I was concerned about how long we could keep delivering excellent customer service without seamless communication and cooperation between the two teams. Just when one manager was making a heated comment about how the sales team fails to follow the set procedures we have in place, the sales manager walked

into the lunchroom. I cringed, waiting for the blow-up I was sure would come. Instead, the sales manager took a deep breath and said, "If you could just see the issues through my eyes, you would understand why I can't follow all the procedures all the time."

I have worked in three organizations in two countries, Japan and the U.S. In each company, I managed both sales and production teams and in each case we had similar disputes. My experiences had conditioned me to believe that these disputes are a natural and healthy process for an organization. However, *Animal Kingdom* has transformed my thinking.

I still believe the diversity between the different groups in my company is important to develop better systems so we can deliver even better customer services. But I am now seeing the importance of getting these two groups to move beyond their differences, to humble themselves, to see through the others' eyes so that more proactive cooperation can take place. *Animal Kingdom* will be required reading for all my co-workers today *and* in the future.

At the heart of *Animal Kingdom* is humility. "Seeing through the eyes of others" requires a humble mind. Seeking to work compatibly to resolve differences requires humility. We can apply the message of *Animal Kingdom* in our homes, in our workplaces, in our politics, and most of all, in our personal lives.

Phil Davis, President, ZenZoeys, Inc.

**A**nimal **K**ingdom

# **Contents**

## Acknowledgments

This book is the brainstorm of Phil Davis, President/CEO of ZenZoeys, Inc. of Salt Lake City, Utah. He suggested I use an animal kingdom as a simple way of communicating challenging ideas about diversity. In writing this book, I decided to use a process called "customer integration." That is, I continued to ask people who read various stages of the manuscript, "How can this book be improved?" As a result, I did multiple revisions and additions. The person who read every version and kept me encouraged and on track is my wife, Katie. Those people who were gracious enough to provide valuable feedback and suggestions include: Danny Guillory, Sue Kwon, Barbara Thompson, Phil Davis, Jessie McCain, Bob Ferguson, Baruti Artharee, and a host of others. The most valuable feedback I received is "make certain all readers are clear that you have used animal groups to convey how we, as individuals and groups, relate to each other in today's world of differences by responding to the discussion questions on page 80." I thank again my editor in residence, Becky Harding. Most of all, I thank the participants in my diversity learning programs for everything they have taught me.

William A. Guillory, Ph.D.

# Animal Kingdom

## Introduction

***Once upon a time***, Utopia was one of the most idyllic places on Earth. Its plains were adorned with meadows, orchards, and a mighty river that was the lifeblood of this magnificent oasis. But all that had changed dramatically in recent years.

Utopia was the name given to the plains by the plant-eating animals because of its seemingly unlimited space and bountiful grasslands. The plains had previously been controlled by large bands of lions that referred to it as the Prideland. They had ruled the plains as far as the eye could see, until the herds began migrating there in large numbers. The herds were dominated by zebra, caribou, and gazelle.

The unchecked population growth of these herds, particularly caribou, had begun to take its toll on the environment. The delicate ecosystem, which had existed for millennia, was seriously out of balance. The regeneration of grasslands was inadequate to feed the growing herd populations and the threat of large-scale starvation was becoming a reality.

Fortunately, the imbalance was not irreversible— but time was of the essence. In spite of the distrust and polarization that existed among the four animal groups, the increasing severity of the situation *required* them to address the system imbalance. They reluctantly agreed to hold a Summit to design a workable solution to address the impending crisis. The Summit was to be scheduled after each animal group held separate meetings of their own to discuss possible solutions.

Would their solutions be in the best interest of them all or would they simply involve their own self interest? Would their pre-Summit positioning involve scheming and sabotage or would their crisis create a sense of urgency to realize the need for mutual understanding and cooperation? Their willingness to change, individually and as groups, would determine which of the two situations would prevail.

In addition to the crisis of the ecosystem, each of the animal groups was experiencing serious internal conflict. These internal strifes were caused by their attempts to adapt to the radically changing attitudes within, and among, their respective groups. Their capacity to resolve these differences would determine the effectiveness of each of their solutions.

However, looming on the horizon was an *unthinkable* threat to Utopia. Mother Earth had her own plan and time frame for restoring balance to the ecosystem. Her plan involved the forces of nature working in the most concerted way to reestablish the abundant condition that once existed. Which of the two resolutions would prevail would depend upon whether or not the animals could achieve the "key to balance" of the ecosystem *within* Mother Earth's time frame.

### Chapter**One**—The Lair

*A*s the lions gathered for their den meeting in preparation for the Summit, there was an air of resolution to address the threatening changes taking place in Utopia. Informal conversations centered on the increasing populations of "dwellers." Dweller was the less-than-complimentary name lions used for the populous herd groups such as zebra, caribou, gazelle, and the other plant-eating animals. Increasingly, more and more of them were populating the plains and infringing on the land typically occupied by lions for roaming, relaxing, and recreation.

King, the leader of the lions, had been listening quietly, but attentively, to the animated discussions among his den members. When King finally stirred, all discussion immediately ceased and they gave him their undivided attention. His first words emphasized the need for a permanent solution to the disturbing events taking place in the kingdom.

"What are we going to do about the herds?" they cried out in unison.

King took a long moment to reply. "Adapt," he said.

"Adapt to what?" they exclaimed.

"We make it look as though we accept them as governing partners of the Prideland," he explained quietly. "Then, we benevolently provide less grassland than needed for their growing populations and allow them to decide the distribution among themselves. The result will automatically be dissension, disputes and, most of all, division."

"You mean the old tried-but-true strategy of 'divide and conquer'?" Lionel asked.

"It's worked in the past, why not today?" commented one of the den members. "After all, we're not dealing with eagles. These are just your basic dwellers. King's plan is brilliant," he concluded.

"No!" King exclaimed. "That strategy is not a long-term solution to our problem. There are too many of them to conquer. We must 'divide and control.' As long as we keep them divided among themselves, we can control the situation and reclaim that which is rightfully ours," King concluded with a self-assuring smile.

Lionel asked, "You mean we have no real intent of sharing governance of the Prideland with the dwellers?"

"Of course not," replied another member of the pride. "What a stupid question!" King just sat back without confirming or discouraging further comment. His point had been made.

Then from the group, Lionheart attracted their attention. He began by saying, "I think there are things we need to consider."

The instant Lionheart began, King suspected trouble. They had rarely seen eye-to-eye on anything, in spite of the fact they were from the same mother— literally brothers. Contrary to Lionheart's warrior nature,

he actually *cared* about the other animals of the kingdom—even dwellers!

However, Lionheart's sensitive nature had been his downfall in becoming King of the Lair. The king needed to be decisive and sometimes ruthless to lead the pride, particularly in times when the plains were ruled according to territorial domination, control, and power.

Lionheart began by pointing out how things had changed over the years since he was a cub. He expressed that living side-by-side with the dwellers was the reality of the present. "We certainly can't get rid of all of them," he mused, "no matter how hungry we are." They all laughed. The comment broke the tension that was beginning to build. "Their numbers are simply overwhelming," he stated with a sense of acceptance. "Any plan, except one that is aimed at side-by-side cooperation and possibly intermingling, will fail in the long term."

The pride listened patiently to Lionheart since they had such respect for him. But when action was necessary, they ultimately abided by the will of their trusted leader. After an extended silence, King replied, "What would you have us do, Brother?"

Lionheart replied, "I, like you, believe we need to adapt. First, we must find a way to halt the increasing migration to the plains and even reduce the present population if we are to reestablish balance to the ecosystem. We hardly have adequate space and food for the herds that presently occupy the plains. We will also have to adapt by learning how to live together compatibly and that will involve intermingling. That is inevitable!"

"It's not inevitable!" King roared. The brotherly nature of the meeting disappeared. An extremely tense silence prevailed as King, on all fours, appeared to be ready for battle. Lionheart held his ground as the two brothers stood eye-to-eye.

After a tense silence, Lionheart replied in a more conciliatory manner, "I am simply pointing out, Brother, that we no longer rule the Prideland. Much of the land we once controlled is grazed by dwellers—except for our secret oasis."

"I know that," King replied, somewhat more relaxed.

"There is more we must consider," Lionheart interjected.

"And what is that?" King inquired, knowing deep down inside he did not want to hear the answer Lionheart would give—an answer that the entire pride knew and most hated to acknowledge.

"The dwellers are no longer afraid of us. Fear will not work anymore. Our strategy to avoid widespread starvation must be one that at least takes into consideration that reality. *We have a legacy of **leadership** to maintain the bountifulness of the plains and the well-being of all who occupy it.* It also includes the wisdom to responsibly adapt to change or we ultimately threaten our own survival. That legacy has been passed

down through countless generations," Lionheart concluded.

"I simply can't see myself associating with dwellers," a den member expressed. "We have so little in common. For example, as any animal knows, we are king of the plains by divine right. There is a natural order to all that exists, and we are at the top of that order! That has never been questioned."

"Until now!" Lionheart bellowed. "Dwellers believe something different. Their attitudes have changed. We have a responsibility to seek solutions that create balance and the well-being of *all* the animals of the plains. Is it possible for us to at least consider, if not respect, their views?" He asked.

"Not if their views infringe upon what is ours by divine right," replied a highly agitated den member. "We need to take increased measures now! If we take away their emergency food supply, it will send a clear message that we are serious about stopping the expanding herd population. That's the only way to deal with dwellers."

"That would cause widespread panic," Lionheart responded.

"So what?" replied the den member. "It's going to happen anyway. We're just speeding up what's inevitable. They only understand action, not words of warning. Perhaps, they'll even start to fear us again." There was a collective look of concern by the Lair that such a measure might be taken. Maintaining control was

quite acceptable, but provoking starvation was a measure most of them were not quite ready to take.

King could see that there was an element of doubt beginning to stir among the den members as the exchanges continued. He thought he might regain the advantage in the discussion by pretending to agree with Lionheart.

He stated, "Brother Lionheart is correct, the dwellers are less fearful of us than in the past; particularly the zebras. We must be very careful of this group. Once they are incited into action, we may lose total control of the situation. In addition, there is no telling what the other dwellers might do if provoked to starvation. They may even band together, which would be an even worse situation."

Lionel stated, "I think there is little chance of that happening as long as we keep them divided. The truth is, they do a good job of creating division without our help."

"You're right as usual, Lionel," King smiled, "but we must also stay one step ahead of what they may be planning."

"How do we do that?" Lionel asked, with a confused look on his face.

King smiled with a knowing glint in his eyes. "I've taken measures to find out what is going on in each of their meetings. I'll know each of their plans within hours of their completion."

When there was a pause among the group, King continued, "Our short-term strategy will be to stop the

expansion of dwellers into the Prideland using whatever tactics are necessary.  There is still a chance that most of them might move on if they know that they will not be accepted."

As they wandered off for the evening, King thought to himself, *I hope I have made the right decision.* In spite of his disagreement with Lionheart, he wanted to do what was best for the pride.  His greatest fear was that his legacy, in the great line of Lion Kings, would be loss of control of the Prideland.  The Prideland had been passed down to him in trust.  His final thoughts that evening were, *I must be certain what the zebras are planning.  If we can control what they do, the other herds will most likely follow placidly.  Controlling the zebras is the key*, he repeated to himself.

*"Shared power and decision making creates a society of equals."*

## Chapter**Two**—The Conclave

*M* eanwhile, the zebras were simultaneously holding a Conclave—an exclusive meeting of invited representatives of the herd. Informal conversation among several zebras focused on the disturbing observation that more and more of them had been disappearing from the herd recently. They had simply wandered off into better grazing land without serious threat from the lions and were never seen again.

The situation was extremely disturbing to the seniors of the herd. They were assembled in a place called the "central location," an open meeting space within the body of the herd, but clearly separate and private. Zebron was the unofficial leader of the herd. That is, he was always the one the lions or the other herds negotiated with when disputes of territorial rights occurred.

Zebron was a veteran of numerous disputes that involved the rights of zebras to graze and prosper wherever they chose. He had earned his reputation and position in the Conclave because of the numerous concessions he had won in such disagreements. Many of the concessions had come about through "direct action" by the zebras, most often in disputes with the lions.

Zebron began the Conclave by requesting that they be led in thanks for the bountiful location upon which they were grazing; particularly, in light of the food conservation program they had all begun.

One of the highly revered Brothers of the Conclave stepped forward. He began his thanks by recounting the history of zebras before they became striped—including the fact that at one time they were spirited stallions with pure black manes. Now being striped, as adaptation to a traumatic history had demanded, they felt the full right to graze in peace among the other animals of the plains.

*They had earned this right as a result of the* **physical resiliency** *they had shown over many generations.* Their physical survival was crowning evidence of their adaptability as a group. Now they were facing new issues of adaptation. He went on to say that if they couldn't collectively create a solution to their present situation that benefited them all, then external forces had a way of *forcing* solutions through crisis. There was no anger or judgment in his remarks. Just the acknowledgment of the progress they had made as zebras and the necessity to address the crisis they faced for the continued well-being of all the animals of the kingdom. He ended by giving thanks for the bountiful location of the Conclave in such troubled times.

The culture of the zebras was firmly imbedded in the traditions that they shared in common: such as the overriding importance of the *welfare* of the herd in preference to self, the inseparable *connection* to the earth that sustained them, and the unrelenting drive for *freedom* to graze in harmony with others.

The leader, Zebron, acknowledged the revered Brother for his thanks and proceeded to address the Conclave. "Brothers and sisters, you all know the crisis we face. The grasslands are receding, our populations are growing, and we face the serious threat of starvation unless we immediately take corrective action. The question I've been praying over is what are we going to do about it?" He immediately bowed his head and went into a trance-like state.

There was absolute silence as Zebron's question hung suspended in the thick air of the Conclave. One of the young sisters of the group looked up and wondered why no one was responding. As she looked around, most of the others pretended they didn't see her questioning look. They continued to graze, knowing that Zebron often started the Conclave with a question that *he* fully intended to answer.

However, before Zebron could begin enlightening the group, the sister, in her naïveté, began to respond to the question he raised. Her name was Zebrala. She was known for making comments or asking questions that no one else dared to raise. Her questions were seemingly naïve, except they went straight to the heart of the matter being discussed. This was the reason she was asked to join the Conclave in the first place.

Apparently not knowing any better, Zebrala responded by posing a question of her own. "What do you mean by what are we going to do about it?" The

herd was stunned. No one had ever answered Zebron's question with a question.

With the patience of an elder, Zebron looked up at her from his trance and responded, "I mean, what action should we take to make sure we don't starve? What's your view, Little Sister?" he asked in a patient manner, taking into account that Zebrala obviously had no respect for protocol—or her elders for that matter!

Zebrala didn't hesitate to respond, "I don't think the problem is what to *do* about our situation. I think the major problem is that we all *think* about our own welfare first, and the other Utopians second."

One of the male zebras raised his head and said, "Are you suggesting that we should think of the welfare of the Others first and ourselves second?"

"No!" she exclaimed. "I think we should think about the welfare of *all* Utopians, period. No first, or second, or third for that matter."

"I don't understand what you mean," bellowed another member of the herd.

"I mean we have to become Utopians before we can truly solve a problem that affects us all," she tried to explain. She had only recently begun exploring this way of thinking. Although it made sense at an intuitive level, she was not quite prepared to rationally explain it to others.

Once of the male zebras, who was known for strong opposition to associating too closely with the Others, had been trying to listen objectively to the exchanges

between Zebrala and the group. At this point, he simply could not graze quietly any longer. He raised his head and bellowed, "What does it mean to become a Utopian? That we blindly *trust* the Others? You forget we have a long history of being treated like the dirt we walk on by the Others, particularly the lions."

Zebrala began by explaining that being a Utopian involved giving up the resistance to extending themselves to the Others because of past injustices. It involved a way of thinking, she explained, where the welfare of *all* the plains animals was the same as the welfare of any *one* group. She paused to see if they understood what she was trying to say.

In response, she received blank stares and even hints of hostility. A few simply began eating again. Zebrala started to panic. At that instant, another brother raised his head and said, "I think we ought to try to understand what Little Sister Zebrala is trying to tell us. The truth is I've been thinking the same kinds of things myself."

The brother who spoke up was Zeb. He had a gentle energy that emanated from his massive body that made others feel comfortable, in spite of his size. He went on, "As most of you know, I am very committed to the teachings of the Earth Mother Gaia. Recently, I've been struggling with the question, 'Who am I?' I have the feeling that there's more to who I am than just being a zebra. So, that's why I'm interested in what Little Sister Zebrala has to say."

Zebrala resumed her sharing, having realized she had connected with a kindred soul in Zeb. "Like Brother Zeb, I believe I am more than just a zebra. If I continue to just think like a zebra and act like a zebra, I'll become the best zebra on the plains. But that's not enough! I want to be more than just a zebra," she declared with her emotions brimming to the top. "I want to be a Utopian!" Zebrala looked over the group for support of her ideas. There was more confusion and curiosity this time, but much less hostility. Here and there, there were even smiles and nods of understanding and agreement.

That's when Brother Zeb, her kindred soul, asked Little Sister if he might repeat what he thought she was saying. Zebrala smiled with relief and said, "I'd be delighted."

"What I think Little Sister is saying is that if we think like Utopians, the solution to our crisis will benefit *all* of us, not just zebras. On the other hand, if we continue to *only* think like zebras, our solution will benefit us most, probably at the *expense* of the Others. Being a Utopian does not mean we have to give up being zebras. Being zebras is our heritage, we can never lose that. But by being Utopians, we can be both."

The last two statements seemed to resonate with most of the Conclave. It was slowly beginning to sink in. But it was disturbing to Zebron. So he raised the question of trust. "How do we know we can trust the Others with *our* best interests? How do we know they will not think of us as weak by extending ourselves and

try to take advantage of us?" he asked the group. There was silence because no one could give definitive assurance.

Then, one of Zebron's followers, Brother Zebrias, who was well respected by the herd, raised his head. He warned that what Little Sister was proposing was not only radical, but placing the herd at great risk, as had been stated earlier by Brother Zebron. "Suppose we extend ourselves to the lions. What do you think the result will be? We must be very careful about what is being proposed here. Most of all, we must ensure the safety of our herd, first and foremost!" he concluded.

One of the most revered elder sisters raised her head and most everyone stopped grazing. She was considered the "heart and soul" of the zebras. She began slowly by recounting all she thought she had heard the others say, particularly, about becoming Utopians. Then she began her own deliberate comments.

"Since The Great Drought, we have migrated endlessly, as a herd, to find a place where we could live in peace with others. We are weary of migration. Separation makes enemies of us all. Connecting places us at risk," she mused. "Quite a dilemma we've created for ourselves, wouldn't you say?"

Brother Zebrias thought to himself, *this is not going well.* He could no longer hold himself in check, so he shouted. "Rather than talking about becoming Utopians, we need to take action by occupying *more* of the grasslands ruled by the lions! Some of us will be sacrificed anyway. We might as well do it for a cause that benefits the herd!"

The revered sister responded levelly, "You know that such a provocation will be viewed as a threat to the lions. And the other herds will see us as troublemakers that may involve repercussions that will adversely affect them."

Zebrias spat back, "So what? We can't depend on the other herds anyway. They have always been first to benefit from our actions even though they never join us upfront." His last comment was followed by an eerie silence as though a truth had been spoken, but no one knew how to respond.

She began slowly in response to Zebrias' accusations, "I guess that's the fix we all find ourselves in when we continue to believe that the old ways are going to solve today's problems. If life has taught us anything, it's that the old ways of isolating ourselves tend to breed suspicion, distrust, and hostility towards others. Moreover, provoking confrontation has led to short-term successes and long-term resentment. We must begin to seek ideas and solutions that create cooperation among all the animals of Utopia. How do we create that level of compatibility? It will involve a level of trust we've never had before. If we don't break the cycle of confrontation, retaliation, and revenge then we're all doomed to a predictable future. And that appears to be a crisis over which we have no control. I only ask that each of us seriously consider everything that's been shared by

everyone. Then look deeply inside ourselves, beyond what we came here believing, because it is there we will collectively discover our way." She sat, and it was clear that the Conclave was complete.

Zebron was visibly moved by the words of the revered sister, as was the entire Conclave. As usual, her way was to "invite" others to look within themselves for the most powerful solutions to the most difficult problems they faced—she referred to this process as discovering "the wisdom beneath the answers." The will of the group appeared to be greater cooperation with the Others to find a solution to their crisis. However, he was not so convinced about their becoming Utopians (Whatever that meant!).

As the Conclave disbanded, a lone zebra moved stealthily through the herd. He thought to himself, *I must find my way to King to discuss the strategy of our Conclave and he, the strategy of his Lair—so we can do what is in the best interests of both our groups.* He was determined that the fate of the zebras would not be in the hands of others! He had sense enough to know you couldn't trust the lions, but you could certainly negotiate for your herd's best interest since they still held the power. The real issue was maintaining their identity as a herd, even if the other naïve zebras didn't understand.

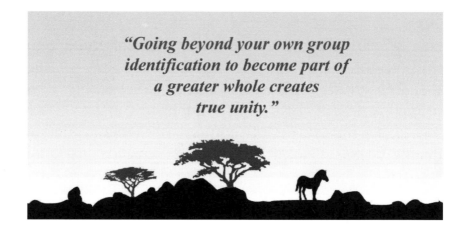

*"Going beyond your own group identification to become part of a greater whole creates true unity."*

## Chapter**Three**—The Gathering of a Few

*C*aribella could feel the excitement and energy of every animal in the herd. *Regardless of the impending crisis they were facing, they were One Caribou, united together*, she thought to herself. *Their survival depended on their solidarity.* They had come from the farthest reaches of the plains to participate in the "Gathering of a Few." This was the name they used for the meeting to discuss solutions to the impending crisis they faced. Caribella began making her way through the herd to greet the elders of the caribou. Off in the distance she spotted Caribon, the wise old leader of their herd. *I must nuzzle him*, she thought to herself and began to work her way in his direction.

As Caribon grazed quietly, he was deep into his own thoughts. Quite frankly, he was weary. The constant migration to find a place where they could be fed, watered, and accepted in their great numbers was continual. He looked up and saw Caribella working her way towards him. She approached him and nuzzled his neck as vigorously and she could. They looked into each other's eyes for what seemed to be an eternity, yet it was only a span of seconds. Little needed to be spoken between the two for they had been the unifying force of the herd in their search for a home. Their search was ended. Utopia was their home. As quickly as she

nuzzled him, she moved on, working her way through the herd before the Gathering began.

As Caribella disappeared from his sight, he was reminded that the old ways were fast disappearing. He knew from centuries of history, passed down from generation to generation, that adaptation was the key to survival. He thought to himself, *it's our **mental toughness** that has sustained us over these difficult times. Now, we are being tested again. Most of all, we must mentally adapt to the different ways of life of the Others. But at what cost,* he thought to himself. *Does **our** culture and way of life mean nothing? We are a proud group with a rich history of accomplishments. We bring our dedication, loyalty, and willingness to earn our way through hard work. What more could the Others want? Nevertheless, these things would be discussed at the Gathering.*

The Caribou believed that Earth Mother Gaia would provide for their needs, no matter what challenges they faced. After all, her message was to populate and replenish the earth. It was hard to understand why those who had so much were opposed to helping those who had so little. Sharing among each other was one of the sacred principles of the Earth Mother. It was the answer to the tremendous growth they were experiencing and the poor living conditions that were setting in. They also believed that if the animals of the plains did not resolve their crisis, then the Earth Mother would. She always created a way for those of the Earth to confront those issues they

chose to ignore. In spite of the challenges they faced, the Caribous were confident the Gathering would resolve these issues.

The Gathering consisted of approximately 40 males and females. Everyone began arriving at the place reserved for the Gathering in the early afternoon and were all assembled by mid-afternoon. The major issue, as the caribou saw it, was *acceptance* by the Others who grazed and hunted on the plains; in particular, the lions. They sought acceptance of their numbers, their culture, and their way of life. As they saw it, once acceptance was achieved, all the other problems they were experiencing would be solved.

Quite spontaneously, and without introduction by agenda, a young, highly spirited male named Carivan raised his head and began speaking. "We are a proud herd with a long history of accomplishments," he bellowed. His eyes were blazing and his nostrils were contracting and expanding in a way that few had ever seen before. The herd was instantly mesmerized by his opening statement.

Carivan continued, "We will not be accepted by the Others until we accept ourselves. We must accept who we are, exactly as we are without trying to artificially be like the Others. Until we realize that we are responsible for the conditions we are experiencing as a herd, there is no hope of acceptance!" An audible reaction of disbelief came forth from the Gathering.

An angry voice from the herd interrupted Carivan and shouted, "We *do* accept ourselves! We have a proud history to prove it. Why do you inflame the Gathering with your nonsense? Your words will only draw attention to us as a herd and arouse the Others! Once the Others accept us as equal, our problems will be solved." The herd stomped in support of the angry voice in opposition to Carivan's statements.

Young Carivan shouted back with equal vehemence, "You fool yourself, my friend! As long as we bow our heads and seek the approval of the Others, we do not accept ourselves!"

Young Carivan paused for effect as he allowed his scorching words to burn into their consciousness. Then he began again. "Are we prepared to contribute to make the plains more habitable for all or do we simply seek a refuge from our past disappointments?" he ended, his eyes blazing with emotion. Carivan had hit a chord, because the herd reluctantly began to stomp in unison.

A female voice from the herd, this one wise and respected, asked, "Are you suggesting we do not contribute to the prosperity of the plains?"

Carivan responded, "I am suggesting, wise and respected one, there is much we have to learn. We are relatively new to these plains as compared to the Others. *We cannot fully find our place until we earn our place!*"

"Your words are true of all of us on the plains, not just caribou," she responded.

"That is true, wise and respected one. However, the Others do not suffer the conditions we experience, placed upon us by the grazing restrictions. We need to see these conditions as *our* problem to solve, not the problem of the Others. Do you agree?" he asked with reverence and respect.

The old wise one paused momentarily, as she considered the shift in burden he was proposing from the Others to the caribou. "What you are saying makes sense. Yet, I wonder if we are able to bear such a responsibility alone. We have never done so before. We have simply migrated when the conditions became too unpleasant," she ended.

"Look to the South," he shouted. "Only barren land as far as the eye can see beyond the bountiful plains. Is migration again our answer?" He allowed that question to hang in the air since he knew how unacceptable it was to everyone.

"The Others will never accept us!" a voice from the Gathering shouted. "The lions hate us, the zebras resent us, and the gazelles ignore us! Even if we do learn to accept ourselves, they will always find a reason to exclude us." The speaker was equally as eloquent and fiery as Carivan.

Carivan was momentarily stopped. After a pause, he looked into the eyes of the speaker and responded, "This Gathering is not about focusing on what the Others think of us, for we have no control of their thoughts. It is about resolving our own crisis. I propose to you, resolution begins from within by first accepting ourselves unconditionally; then partnering with others to create solutions that benefit us all."

In response, the fiery young speaker challenged Carivan's proposal. "We're better off keeping to ourselves. If we partner with the others, particularly the zebras, the lions will make it even more difficult for us to get more grassland. I've had conversations with some of the zebra elders. They have little interest in intermingling with us. They think we are weak and spineless because we don't choose to be troublemakers like them."

Carivan responded, "We all have our different ways of responding to crisis. They may use 'direct action' and we may use 'patience.' Who is to say which is best? I am not sure who has that depth of wisdom to know what is best for another." He paused to let his words sink into the minds of those assembled.

*This was not the way the Gathering was supposed to begin,* thought Caribella. She had been working her way to the center to begin the proceedings when young Carivan had simply upstaged the agenda with his inflammatory opening.

Carivan continued, his energy upped to even greater proportions than when he began, "How do we accept who we are?" he asked the Gathering.

Then, in reply, someone in the herd asked in return, "How?"

So Carivan repeated his question again, this time much louder, "How do we accept who we are?"

Again, the herd's reply was, "How?"

He asked a final time, and the sound of the reply, "How?" resonated for miles along the plains in all directions.

"By fully developing and contributing our talents to making Utopia better than what it is now," he replied. We must use our numbers to fuel a new way of life, without sacrificing who we are!"

"So," Carivan exhorted, "we have come full circle. We cannot be accepted by the Others, until we accept ourselves as being fully capable, able, and highly contributing members of Utopia. We control our own destiny, but we must consciously choose to be self-determining." As quickly as he had captured the attention of the Gathering, he disappeared into the herd with his final words.

Caribella had finally reached the central place, but Carivan was gone. So there she stood with everyone still spellbound by his inspiring words. Before she realized it, wise old Caribon was by her side. The two of them attempted to harness the fervor of the Gathering from the elevated level that Carivan had taken it. He raised his head slightly, which she acknowledged and moved a short distance aside.

Caribon stood there silently for what seemed like an eternity to the Gathering. Finally he began, "I know there will be much discussion of the words shared with us by the young, spirited Carivan." The herd began stomping at the mention of his name. Caribon realized the fervor had not subsided. If anything, they were waiting for a sign, a direction, and a vision. They were waiting for action.

In response he blurted out spontaneously, "Carivan has set our direction! He has set our agenda! He has defined our vision!" The herd went wild. Upon which a steady chant began resonating from the herd. Carivan! Carivan! Carivan!

The young male caribou, Carivan, reappeared as mysteriously as he had disappeared at the central place with Caribon. Caribon nodded for Caribella to join them as a show of One Caribou. She did, and the herd went wild!

Caribon thought to himself, *if we could convince the gazelles to join our cause and secure a partnership with the zebras, our problems would be solved. That will be our strategy.* How to approach the gazelles was significantly more delicate than the partnership with the zebras. *If only I knew how the gazelles felt about the present crisis. We must find a way to approach them before the Summit.* Whatever they were deciding in their meeting was the key to the caribou solution, since the gazelles were so well respected by the other herds. Somehow, Earth Mother would provide a way to make the connection; he knew it in his heart.

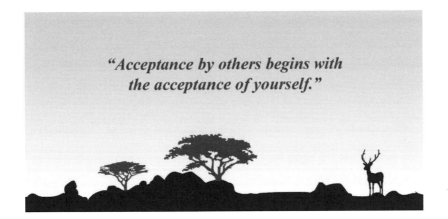

*"Acceptance by others begins with the acceptance of yourself."*

# Animal Kingdom

## ChapterFour—The Ceremony

*T*he gazelles chose to be as separate from the "Plainlanders" as possible. Plainlanders was the common name the gazelles used for other animals of the plains. It was in their nature not to draw attention to themselves. They were tightly knit with strong disciplined behavior in behalf of the herd. They viewed themselves as one, with little attention drawn to their individual roles.

Although they were thought of as dwellers by the lions, they considered themselves separate, distinct, and perhaps superior in ways the Plainlanders could not understand. It mattered little what the others thought of them. The more they were a mystery to the Plainlanders, the better. However, they were not *completely* separate from the other animals of the plains. Some of their herd grazed in the common area—making contact with the others inevitable. In spite of this situation, they tried to have the least association with the others of a nature that would influence their traditions in any way.

The gazelles had chosen a remote area to hold their meeting; toward the northern end of the plains. They considered their gathering to be a sacred occasion since the spiritual was never considered separate from any activity. In fact, they called their meeting "The Ceremony" to signify the formal, solemn nature of the occasion. This practice of including the spiritual in their day-to-day activities was viewed as how things were meant to be in the grand scheme of The Way.

The Way was an instinctive source of knowing that guided the herd in its decisions and day-to-day behaviors. It was as intimately tied to their lives as their hides to their bodies. The Elders of the herd were entrusted with guiding the other gazelles in revealing The Way. The Way could be described as a "homing pattern" that each member of the herd knew by trusting their natural instincts. When such was the case, they operated as a "symphony of one."

The Ceremony was held in a beautiful open alcove surrounded by trees. They sat in a circle to conduct the proceedings. The agenda called for several preliminary activities prior to discussion of the Agreement. The Agreement outlined the strategy of the gazelles in addressing the situation involving the food supply, increasing herd population, and imbalance of the ecosystem. It was created by the Most Honorable Gazellim, the senior Elder.

The agenda was prepared in advance and each participant knew his role. As a result, much of what was to be discussed had already been decided before the meeting. The Ceremony was to be the occasion for official confirmation.

One of the eldest and most trusted members of the gazelle gathering was unable to travel to The Ceremony, so he dispatched one his brightest warriors, Gazellong, to attend in his place. Gazellong was known for his bravery

which had been displayed on many occasions. He spoke his mind, but was respectful and reverent to his elders.

In spite of the fact that everyone had received the Agreement in advance, the Secretariat was asked to remind everyone present of the highlights as a formality. After the presentation by the Secretariat, Gazellim asked for questions. None were asked or expected since The Ceremony was considered to be the occasion for formal confirmation. When Gazellim called for a vote, each of the attendees indicated their approval by an almost imperceptible nod. The first sign of tension occurred when Gazellong's turn came to ratify the Agreement. Instead of nodding, as the others had done, he sat there with a look of indecision. It was extremely rare that anyone would question the wisdom of the Most Honorable Elder. The silence was deafening.

There was no panic in the meeting since panic was inappropriate. There was only the slightest eye movement of disapproval by those in attendance, particularly Gazellim. He asked softly of Gazellong, "Do you not agree with our report for dealing with the precarious situation we face, Honorable Gazellong?"

He replied, "I only hesitate, Most Honorable One, because I wonder if we can continue to isolate ourselves from the Plainlanders *and* ensure our survival and security."

"Do you agree we have done so successfully over many generations?" asked Gazellim.

"Yes, I do," he replied softly, with respect and reverence. "However, we are small in number compared to the others and limited to the grasslands allotted to us by agreement with the lions and the other herds. I also fear what might happen to us if the Plainlanders unite and we remain isolated—unless our course is to migrate again."

The elder Gazellim was adamant that they would never migrate again. He even showed the slightest emotion in response, but quickly regained control of himself.

Given the courage shown by Gazellong by raising questions about the Agreement, the second Elder in seniority asked, "Most Honorable One, may I speak?"

Gazellim was somewhat surprised by the unusual request and was inclined to simply ignore it. However, he realized that he had, in fact, opened the discussion by inviting Gazellong's comments. He gave his consent to the Second Elder.

"I do not believe we need to be concerned about our security. In spite of our small numbers, we are dealing with less than highly intelligent types. After all, they are not eagles, merely Plainlanders." He paused to gather his thoughts and allow the chuckling to subside. "As long as we ensure our grazing area, separate and apart from the Plainlanders, we are secure. If there is any group we must stay alert for, it is the lion. I am certain their motive is to control Utopia by whatever means necessary," he ended.

Another respected Elder asked to be recognized. Gazellim bowed his head to indicate permission. He began, "I believe it is vital that we understand the motives of the Plainlanders in order to maintain our security. Such knowledge requires a certain amount of intermingling to understand their ways."

"Is it possible for us to also be changed by such intermingling?" Gazellim asked the respected Elder.

"With our discipline, I am confident it is unlikely," the respected Elder replied.

Gazellim shifted his eyes to Gazellong, the warrior, to see if he still had questions about the Agreement. He asked, "Are there any other issues regarding the impending crisis that concern us?" Although his question was open to response by any of them, he directed it to Gazellong.

"Yes, Most Honorable One. There are other issues that concern us. First, I do not believe separate coexistence is in our best interest. I believe that we are destined to discover the key to balance of the ecosystem and make it a reality." Gazellong continued when given permission by Gazellim's slight eye movement. "We should extend ourselves to understand the ways of the Plainlanders and encourage them to understand ours. It is only through mutual understanding and cooperation that our future can be secure."

"You do realize that what you propose may change our Way as well as theirs," Gazellim noted.

Gazellong simply nodded his understanding and replied, "Such change is inevitable if we are to discover the key to balance that will resolve our crisis."

Gazellim continued, "It may even lead to crossbreeding. Is crossbreeding acceptable to you, Honorable Gazellong?"

He responded immediately, "No, it is not, Most Honorable One. The Plainlanders do not understand us or our Way. However, some degree of crossbreeding may be beyond our control."

The Most Honorable One paused while gathering his thoughts. He scanned the faces of the others to determine if there was more to be said. As he established eye contact, each of them looked downward. It was clear that the highly unusual exchange of ideas was complete. It had also significantly changed the present Agreement. Gazellim began, *"We have survived over millennia by our **intelligence and wisdom** of The Way. These are both **spiritual** values that have served to guide our decisions when the rationality and reason of opposing points of view have been neutral."*

He paused again and appeared to go into a deeper state of thoughtfulness and began again, "We find ourselves at such an impasse again with the present situation. If we are forced to intermingle, it must be with those with whom we have the most in common, as well as with whom we can form a partnership." He paused to consider his observations before going on, "It would appear that it is in our best interest to extend ourselves to

the families of zebra and caribou of all the animals of the plains." He stopped to visually poll The Ceremony representatives and received unanimous agreement. "This strategy would appear to best preserve our security and way of life," he ended wearily.

The Most Honorable Elder Gazellim sat alone in the sacred circle meditating for some time after the others had gone. At the conclusion of his meditation, he reasoned, *we must begin our strategy as soon as possible. Swift and decisive action is a necessity once a course has been determined.* With these thoughts, he decided how their strategy would be put into action and who would be his trusted emissary.

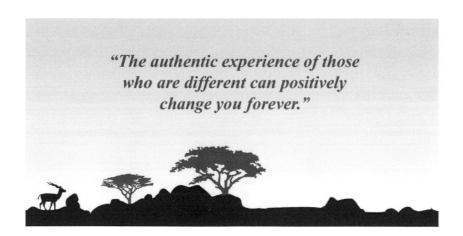

*"The authentic experience of those who are different can positively change you forever."*

### Chapterr**Five**—The Emissary

*O*n the day following The Ceremony, the Most Honorable Gazellim dispatched Gazellong, the warrior, to explore a meeting with the zebra and caribou. When Gazellong approached the zebra camp, he felt the hot stares of suspicion, caution, and curiosity. When he made eye contact with a zebra fearless enough to confront him, Gazellong asked, "Where might I find your Most Honorable Elder?"

The fearless zebra was, at first, confused. Then he understood that Gazellong must have been asking about Zebron, the leader of the zebras. The zebra turned his head in the direction of the central location of the herd. As Gazellong approached the central location, Zebron was conducting a meeting with his trusted council.

Zebrias immediately challenged Gazellong's presence in their camp and his brazen interruption of their council meeting. Their eyes locked. However, Zebrias quickly noticed that there was no fear in the eyes of the warrior gazelle. Other gazelles were usually humble and quickly dropped eye-to-eye contact. However, this one radiated neutrality and quiet confidence.

Zebron immediately recognized the presence of a warrior. He bowed his head to welcome the stranger. Gazellong bowed lower in return, which went unnoticed by the others. The lower bow was Gazellong's

---

acknowledgment of another herd's highest elder—a sign of respect that was clearly obvious to the zebra leader. Zebron paused, recognizing an unspoken request for a private meeting. Then he turned to his council members to ask if they might resume their meeting after he conducted business with their uninvited guest. The council recognized the question as a request and quickly dispersed among the herd. However, one of his trusted council members remained within listening range of Gazellong and Zebron.

"I am Gazellong of the gazelle herd. I am honored to have you receive me on such short notice." He paused as if to gather his thoughts then came quickly to the point. "I have been sent by my Most Honorable Elder to ask if it is possible for us to work together to resolve the impending food shortage and restore balance to the ecosystem."

Zebron replied, "How might we accomplish such a challenge? My council and I have been discussing this question and, quite frankly, we have not found a solution."

Gazellong responded, "Perhaps our problem is attempting to find a solution that involves us all by holding separate councils."

"But won't the Summit bring us together in that way?" Zebron questioned.

"Not exactly," the warrior replied. "It's one thing to hold separate meetings and develop our own strategies that benefit us, often at the expense of others. On the

other hand, it's a completely different process to attempt to *understand* some other group's values, needs, and fears *common to our own*. We call it, 'seeing through the eyes of others.' That is what my Most Honorable Elder is inquiring of you."

Zebron was stunned! He had never experienced a negotiation where the zebras' well-being was considered by the Others. He began slowly, "To be honest, I have never experienced another group truly attempting to understand our concerns." Zebron became aware of his growing respect for Gazellong. He asked, "How does your Most Honorable Elder propose we accomplish this level of trust?" Zebron instantly recalled their Conclave where he raised the question of trusting the Others. He also noticed that what Gazellong called 'seeing through the eyes of others' was the key to achieving that level of trust.

"It is not difficult," he replied, "if we are willing to honestly share our values, needs, and fears with each other. The difficulty is that we may feel vulnerable in doing so."

"How do we know that the Others will not take advantage of our fears?" Zebron inquired.

Gazellong replied, "We do not know whether they will or will not attempt to take advantage of our fears. We must be willing to extend trust to each other. If we do not, I fear true resolution of our impending crisis will be impossible." Then, recalling his haunting dream of the previous night he said, "I also fear we may suffer an

even greater catastrophe if we do not work together for a solution that is in the best interest of us all. My Most Honorable Elder feels we have no choice. That is why I was sent to you."

"When can I meet with your Most Honorable Elder?" Zebron asked.

"As soon as we can arrange a meeting," Gazellong replied, "since time is of the essence. However, we must first journey to the caribou to enroll their inclusion. They are even more impacted by the threat of starvation than we are."

Zebron was wary of the inclusion of the caribou. It seemed that in prior disputes, the zebras and caribous were often in competition.

Noticing Zebron's hesitation, Gazellong asked, "Should we discuss the involvement of the caribou first, before seeking their inclusion?"

"I am not sure," Zebron answered. "We have always competed with the caribou for resources in the past. I am not certain if I can extend trust to them and I also question *their* willingness to extend trust to us."

"All we can do is invite their participation and see what happens. Somehow, I think we face an urgency that requires us all to look beyond our suspicions of each other," Gazellong replied. He paused and looked gravely at Zebron, "We are facing a crisis that may threaten our very existence! And I assure you time is of the essence!"

"Perhaps you're right," Zebron responded in a pensive manner, wondering what insights Gezellong had

that he was not revealing. "Our compromises of the past have certainly not worked over the long term. Maybe it's time we tried something *really* different, no matter how vulnerable it feels. Let's invite them."

"Since you have dealt with the caribou before, who should we approach for our invitation?" Gazellong asked.

"There's no question there," responded Zebron, "Old Caribon. He and I have 'locked horns' many times. And as you can see, I don't have any horns, but he does," Zebron laughed.

As Gazellong and Zebron began making their way to the caribou herd, the trusted council member who remained within listening range of the conversation decided it was time to meet again with King of the lions to plan their strategy.

נ

As Gazellong and Zebron approached the caribou herd, there was immediate communication throughout of their visit. The old wise one, Caribon, came forward to greet them. He welcomed them to the herd and smiled cautiously at Zebron, his worthy adversary of many disputes.

Gazellong spoke first, explaining his mission as directed by his Most Honorable Elder. He described his meeting with Zebron and his willingness to explore the idea of "seeing the world through the eyes of others." He ended by stating that he was extending a similar

invitation to the caribou to join in a meeting to resolve their impending crisis of starvation.

"We would be excited to join in your meeting," Caribon stated without reservation. He eyed Zebron suspiciously and asked, "Are you willing to see the world through our eyes, my striped friend?"

Zebron flinched noticeably, but responded with the greatest of diplomacy, "Why of course, my aging friend."

*"Reconciling differences begins with seeing through the eyes of others."*

William A. Guillory, Ph.D.

## Chapter**Six**—The Alliance

*T*he Most Honorable Gazellim hosted the meeting. Each of the senior representatives was allowed to bring only one of their most trusted advisors. Zebron brought Brother Zebrias, the well-respected elder. Caribon brought Caribella, the rock of the caribou. And the Most Honorable Gazellim was advised by his emissary, Gazellong. The senior representatives sat in an inner circle, and their respective advisors sat behind them, forming an outer circle.

Gazellim began by thanking each of the elders for agreeing to explore the possibility of a solution to their crisis—a solution that would benefit all the animals of the plains, including the lions. He was visibly delighted that the meeting was taking place so quickly. *It's all falling into place according to our plan*, he thought to himself. Then, quite unexpectedly, Brother Zebrias insisted that he be acknowledged. This occurrence was a total surprise to Zebron who looked highly upset at the junior member of his delegation.

The Most Honorable Gazellim, the host, nodded gratuitously for Brother Zebrias to have the attention of the others. Zebrias collected himself, as the elder he presumed himself to be, and began, "I realize I was invited to this meeting as an advisor to Brother Zebron." Zebron flinched at the mention of his name in concert with any comments that Zebrias was about to make. "On most matters which are vital to the welfare of our herd, we are in 100% agreement. However, in this matter of an alliance against the lions, I think we are about to make a grave error. We should *all* meet in good faith, without this conspiracy, to do what is best for each of our groups. That was our agreement." He paused to sense how the group was responding to his comments. At best, their responses were neutral. *Not as I expected*, he thought to himself. He began again, with a decidedly different tact, "Although I completely support the objectives of this alliance, I simply felt compelled to express my sense of a lack of integrity for what we are attempting to do, without the participation of the lions. Thank you for allowing me to be acknowledged." Then he sat in his place outside of the inner circle.

Brother Zebrias was not naïve or stupid. He simply saw the world solely through the eyes of a zebra. Any scope beyond that world was not part of his reality. Zebron appeared to be in a state of embarrassment and shock.

After Zebrias completed his statements, Gazellim took the edge off of the meeting by commenting, "Any alliance to achieve a solution that benefits us all will have many points of view. We thank Honorable Brother Zebrias for his comments that we must consider carefully." He then stated, "If there are no objections, I suggest we take a break." Upon which all agreed, and they each went into private consultation with their trusted advisor.

ℿ

During the break, Zebron and Zebrias had a heated discussion, with Zebron doing most of the talking. Afterwards, Zebron walked over to the Most Honorable Gazellim and whispered something privately. Gazellim reconvened the meeting. When all were assembled again, he indicated that Brother Zebrias would not be remaining, but he did want to say a few words before leaving.

Brother Zebrias apologized for his outburst of opinion, given his position at the meeting. He further apologized for any embarrassment he might have caused to Brother Zebron. He acknowledged that they had not discussed positions the alliance might take or if the alliance would become a reality. He concluded, "Since I have embarrassed both myself and my senior representative, I ask to be excused from this meeting. I want each of you to know, particularly my Brother Zebron, I fully support any, and all, decisions made by this alliance." Then he left.

The Most Honorable Gazellim began by reassuring the alliance that brother Zebron had promised that the matter of Brother Zebrias would be "handled" when he returned to his herd. He stated, "In truth, there are probably similar types in each of our herds but there should be no problem of the alliance's plan being made known to the lions. In any case, we haven't made any specific plans for action to be taken by the alliance."

Caribon stirred and Gazellim recognized him with a nod. Caribon smilingly asked, "Have you noticed that you referred to us as the 'Alliance' twice in your last comments and once before the break?"

Gazellim smiled and replied, "I guess I picked up on the name given to us by the comments of the Honorable Brother Zebrias. So, we are officially the 'Alliance,' " he declared. All of the representatives burst out in either whinnying or stomping as they celebrated their unity as a group.

Gazellim got everyone's attention again and posed the question to the others, "What do we do about the situation we face in terms of impending starvation and the imbalance of the ecosystem?"

Caribon was first to respond. "It's very simple. We need more grasslands for our herds—grasslands now controlled by the lions."

Zebron responded, "The lions would say we need to control migration and population growth, no matter how much land we have."

"How can we keep others out of this paradise or limit the offspring of our herds? These are matters of the Earth Mother Gaia," Caribon appealed.

Gazellim could see that Zebron and Caribon were revisiting a well-rehearsed conversation. They both looked to him for a response that would resolve their impasse. Gazellim began slowly, "No matter how bountiful the plains are, there is a natural herd limitation that can be supported to achieve the balance we require.

If that limitation is exceeded, we will all suffer the consequences, lions or no lions. The matter of population control and land management is not a problem caused by the lions." They all began to realize that there were serious issues to be resolved among themselves that had little to do with the lions—issues that involved *fundamental differences* in their own historical traditions.

Gazellim continued, "In truth, we are primarily responsible for the imbalance of the ecosystem. We have not managed the sensible consumption of the rich grasslands or allowed sufficient time for their full regeneration. These are issues *we* must address. Our solutions must exceed each of our herd's self-interests. They must benefit us all, including the lions. I believe we each have an outstanding characteristic that when combined for our collective benefit is the key to resolving our crisis. Do you agree?" he asked, looking at both Zebron and Caribon.

It slowly began to dawn on both Caribon and Zebron that Gazellim had taken the discussion to a whole new level of resolution. A level that was clearly beyond what they had expected to encounter in the meeting.

After a period of silence, which seemed like an eternity to each of them, Caribon turned to Zebron and asked, "You have more herd than the gazelle and less than the caribou. What would you propose be done to responsibly manage ourselves?"

Zebron looked at them both. "We must begin by turning away those who migrate onto the plains from

other places. We simply do not have the resources to accommodate them all." He paused, realizing his next statements would affect them all. "We must design a system for reducing the number of herds from all the animals already here by inviting them to migrate to new regions, possibly to the east or west. I have no idea how this is to be accomplished," he concluded with his head bowed.

Gazellim raised a question. "Perhaps there are those among us with an exploring nature that may have an inclination to move on. There may be more of them than we think."

As the discussion continued and a plan for herd reduction began evolving, it was clear that the cooperation of the lions was essential. They also realized that the lions had generations of experience in land management, acquired when they ruled the Prideland.

By the end of the second day, they agreed to a plan they felt confident would benefit all the animals of the plains. Gazellong was again the emissary sent to inform the lions that they were prepared for the Summit. He was also instructed to keep secret the formation of the Alliance or the tentative conclusions they had reached.

₪

Gazellong was received by King the following day. The warrior gazelle explained to King that he had visited each of the other herds and they both expressed a

readiness to convene the Summit. He went on to express the feeling that time was of the essence. At that point, he began to notice the detachment that King had to his message of urgency.

King asked, "Is what you express the unanimous opinion of the gazelle, zebra, and caribou leaders?"

"Yes, it is, Most Honorable King," Gazellong replied. He wondered if there was more to King's question, as though he had knowledge of the Alliance.

"Let me pose the question of a time and place to my Lair and I will send you a reply sometime during the coming week," King stated in an unconcerned manner.

Gazellong could see that their meeting was concluded, so he bowed graciously and departed. It was difficult for him to understand why King did not have the same sense of urgency as the other groups.

₪

When Gazellong was safely out of sight, King summoned Zebrias. "So, they've formed an Alliance in opposition to the lions, you say," King asked Zebrias.

"Yes. I only chose to stay for the beginning of the meeting. When I realized what they were planning, I asked to be excused so that I might inform you of their strategy. Unfortunately, I do not know what they have planned as an Alliance," Zebrias responded.

"No need," replied King with a smug look. "I have other sources in each of the herds where nothing is secret.

I am fully aware of the plan they have. The usual solution of demanding more of the Prideland, instead of limiting their numbers and tending to the land," King roared, in a highly agitated state.

Zebrias was so frightened he thought King might have him for supper instead of inviting him to the oasis he had promised. Then King turned to Zebrias and said, "There is one final favor I have to ask of you."

"And what is that?" Zebrias asked, clearly frightened of King's mood.

"I want you to return to your herd of zebras. Tell Zebron that you suspect the gazelles have created a separate agreement with the lions for unlimited grasslands and protection from the Others. Tell him the agreement is in exchange for their support of the lions' refusal to provide any additional grasslands to the other herds. When you have completed this task, return to spend the rest of your days in an oasis beyond your wildest imagination," King smiled.

₪

Zebrias returned to the zebra camp to deliver King's message, and was never seen or heard from again.

*"Cooperation is the key to designing creative solutions where major differences are involved."*

## Chapter**Seven**—The Great Flood

*W*hen the rains first began, they seemed to be a blessing from the heavens. Earth Mother Gaia had answered their prayers, thought the caribou. Now we will have life-giving nourishment for the grasslands and there will be enough food for all. A spontaneous celebration took place as the caribou danced in the bountiful rainfall.

The sign of rain was more ominous in the gazelle camp. Gazellong had had a disturbing dream the night after the Ceremony. He dreamed of a great flood that had resulted from a continual downpour that lasted several weeks. He awakened himself from the dream to avoid seeing the result. The next morning he recounted the dream to the Most Honorable Gazellim. They both doubted the dream was a sign to warn them of impending danger, since most dreams are rarely literal.

After much discussion, they concluded that an occurrence of a major flood was highly unlikely. This was after all the rainy season, they both reasoned. Where would such waters come from, sufficient to flood the plains? No need to alarm everyone with a premonition that could not be proved. The dream *did,* however, prompt sufficient enough concern to immediately initiate the joint meeting among the major herds that resulted in the Alliance.

ﬢ

King had offered to have the Summit in one of the beautiful alcoves that none of the other groups had ever seen. This invitation was overwhelmingly rejected by the herds because of their long-standing distrust of the lions. The lions interpreted the rejection of their invitation as a sign that emotions were running too high and they all needed to cool off before coming together to resolve the situation.

The caribou, who felt most vulnerable to the threat of starvation were, in fact, becoming desperate about the situation. When the herds suggested an alternative location to hold the Summit that would neutralize the power of the lions, the lions, in turn, deemed it to be unsuitable. Since that time, suggestions by both camps were either rejected by one side or the other. Thus, a resulting stalemate existed when the showers spontaneously erupted with no advance warning.

₪

A week after the rains began, the downpour continued. Water was beginning to collect on the plains and there were puddles everywhere. The mighty river had swollen into a raging torrent that threatened to overrun its banks, causing even greater flooding. The caribou had long since stopped celebrating the downpour. The zebras, who were a superstitious group, had an ominous feeling about the rains that showed no sign of ending. The gazelles had finally decided that

Gazellong's dream was, in fact, a premonition of impending danger and began to move closer to the other herds in case emergency action needed to be taken. The only area of higher ground was the mountain territory of the lions. The lions simply moved to the upper ledges as they watched the situation unfold on the plains below. The thought of a Summit was the last thing on any of their minds.

₪

Then, the unthinkable happened. Far to the north, where the plains began, was a giant mountain lake that had existed for centuries. This lake was the source of the mighty river that flowed so majestically through Utopia. It was bound by a high wall of mountains that kept it safely contained from the plains below.

Only rare times in history are such walls unable to withstand the swollen pressures of millions of gallons of water. When filled to the brim, the pressures exerted throughout the lake against the mountain walls become immense. In such situations, nature flows with that which is inevitable. Slowly, foot-by-foot, the upper mountain walls began to weaken. Then, with an unannounced mighty burst that could be heard for miles, the upper walls willingly gave way.

The animal groups heard the sound of the breakthrough off in the distance and instinctively realized that the waters of the huge mountain lake would soon

flood the plains where they grazed. They had little time to reach higher ground or be swept away by the deluge. The panic was on. Only self-preservation mattered, even among members of the same animal groups.

Tons of water poured through the opening of the upper mountain wall and swept down the mountainside clearing everything in its path. Fortunately, the breakthrough was contained to the very top mountain elevations.

₪

The mountain territory of the lions was the last remaining symbol of the Prideland. All the herds had respected this area, since it was known to be special to the lions. It was several miles long and consisted of a number of perches where they could see great distances on the plains.

As the zebras headed toward the mountain territory in a confused panic, Zebrala pulled Zeb aside. She quickly told him of a narrow mountain pass that she had seen when grazing near the lion's territory. She suspected that it might be a route to safety. He whinnied as loud as he could in the midst of the total confusion of zebras running in all directions with no thought in mind except survival. Without access to a route to higher ground, their attempt of ascending to safety was hopeless.

Zeb got the attention of a few of the more rational zebras in the midst of the panic, and he and Zebrala

began leading a small band toward the mountain pass. En route, they encountered Carivan and a small group of caribou attempting to find their way to safety. Zeb explained to Carivan that they were attempting to find a mountain pass to higher ground. In the midst of the confusion, Carivan's group of caribou was faced with a split-second decision: join the zebra band or find their own way to safety. As much out of instinct as the trust established when survival is at stake, Carivan's group banded with the zebras to follow the intuition of Zebrala.

₪

Meanwhile, the strongest and swiftest of the gazelles had reached the herds who were hopelessly seeking higher ground. All they observed was confusion and panic. The weak and most of the young of the gazelle herd, who lagged far behind along the way, were left to the mercy of the flowing waters.

The gazelles were led by Gazellong, the warrior. They all trusted his instincts to lead them to safety. But right now, his instincts were failing him as he realized he knew little of this terrain. They had always tried to be as isolated as possible from the rest of the Plainlanders. At the very least, Gazellong's instincts told him, if there was any hope of survival; it would be here where higher ground existed.

₪

As Zebrala tried to get her bearings to lead the band to the mountain trail, the chaos prevented her from getting a clear field of vision of the mountainside. Markers that she had previously known were either obscured or totally washed away. It appeared that the band was wandering around in circles. Zeb stepped forward at this point. He communicated to Zebrala, "Little Sister, I *know* you can do this. Just focus on what the place looked like in your mind's eye before the rain began. Ignore what the terrain looks like now. Try to block out all the confusion around you. I promise no harm will come to you."

Little Sister Zebrala smiled, closed her eyes, and allowed her intuition to take over her thinking. A prior picture of the bountiful, peaceful plains came to her mind. She began to move in response to that visualization. It was as though the path was being created moment-by-moment as she led them through the maze by pure instinct. Wherever she stepped forward, a clearing magically appeared. Even Zeb was stunned by the ease of her movements once she allowed her intuition to take over. She moved toward the mountain with an amazing sense of surety. Then the magic disappeared! Her eyes flew open as if being awakened from a deep sleep. Disorientation set in again, just when it appeared they were about to succeed.

"Something is missing," she blurted out to Zeb.

"What do you mean?" he asked.

"I don't know what I mean. I just know that something is missing. Until we can find out what it is, I can't be as confident as I was before. I'm simply saying the picture disappeared because something is missing!"

"Little Sister, this is no time for indecision," Zeb exhorted, appearing to lose his confidence in her momentarily. Then, regaining his composure, he said, "We are losing our herd as the water rises. Soon it won't matter whether your intuition is working or not. Why don't you just *guess* from where we are now? The mountain is so near, we can't possibly miss the trail."

Out of desperation, Zebrala began leading them again, hoping that some rational clue would appear since her intuition had simply shut down.

₪

When Gazellong and his band of gazelles attempted to navigate their way toward the mountains, they quickly discovered that the other herds had the same intention. As they made their way through the confusion, the floodwaters continued to rise at an alarming rate. The young and weak were either run over by the adult animals or pulled under by the rapidly flowing waters. Survival dominated the consciousness of the herds.

He looked back, only to discover that his band of gazelles was becoming more dispersed among the other confused herds. Many had simply given in to their appointed fate. His own faith wavered momentarily as

he considered the value of his own survival without the survival of the other gazelles. He thought to himself how easy and inviting it would be to give in to the will of The Way, as his Elders had chosen. They had not even bothered to flee the site of The Ceremony with the gazelle herd when the rains began. At that instant, a shattering thought intruded deep within his consciousness that he had a mission to accomplish. It was not his time to go the way of the Elders. His path would be guided to safety. Those of his band who chose to persevere were the ones needed, and those who did not were subject to their chosen fate.

He and his band, which were intent upon surviving, appeared to move through the confused mass as though guided by a force greater than them. Although the confusion around them persisted, they navigated their way as in a slipstream, without effort.

₪

The flooding reached knee high and some of the smaller and older animals began to give way to the inevitable. Some tried swimming in the river as a means of survival since they knew it so well. However, the river was not a friend today. It was a raging torrent following the orders of the "forces of nature." Then it happened again! Another explosion far to the north signaled the final breakthrough of the lower elevation of the mountain lake boundaries. The waters rushed out at

an amazing speed toward the plains where the confused animals were desperately seeking refuge.

At the sound of the second breakthrough, the herds began running in all directions in an even greater panic. Sensing that their only hope for survival was high ground, they tried more desperately to scale the mountain, but to no avail. The mountain was steeply banked and consisted of rugged slippery rock at its base. When a few successfully made it a short distance up the mountain steep, they came tumbling down on the others trying to make similar valiant efforts. They felt trapped, confused, and hopeless. It appeared their fate was destined by the forces of nature. In this case, a quick submersion below the murky waters was a welcome, peaceful ending. Most of their last thoughts were a confused jumble of questions, all beginning with the word "Why."

מ

Through the torrents of rain and flooding, Gazellong noticed the small band of caribou and zebra making their way towards the mountain in a somewhat organized manner. By instinct, he began following their path.

When Gazellong's group caught up with the band of caribou and zebra, he noticed that they were being led by a young female zebra. Again Zeb, flanked by Carivan, stepped forward and explained to Gazellong their attempt to find a mountain pass to higher ground. The bonding between the three leaders was instantaneous. It was as though the piece of the puzzle had finally been put into place that would destine their survival. Without any hesitation, Gazellong instructed his band of surviving gazelles to join the zebra and caribou.

The instant Gazellong declared his alliance with the zebra and caribou herds, Zebrala regained her confidence. The gazelles were the missing piece. The magic of her intuition snapped in again as she resumed her quest to find the mountain pass. This time she did not need the encouragement of Zeb. Her inner guidance was clear and strong. All ambiguity and doubt disappeared.

Just then, up ahead, Zebrala saw the partially washed out trail that led upwards to safety. She had forgotten how well camouflaged the trail was and that it was hidden by a heavy growth of trees at its base. If there was no prior knowledge of the trail, it would be impossible to find.

Zebrala had discovered the trail quite by accident when she had noticed a mixed group of herds from the common grazing area disappear into the thick foliage that hid the mountain pass. The common area was the lush land provided by the lions to all the herds to graze together.

What Zebrala had not revealed was the extent to which she was influenced by those who grazed in the

common area.    It was their view that compatibility among the herds through intermingling and understanding was the way of the future.

The surviving band of zebras, caribous, and gazelles began the trek up the mountain pass, which became easier as they ascended to higher ground. They stopped momentarily to look back on the flooded plains. The torrent from the second breakthrough carried animal herds of all types to their final fate. No distinction was made because of differences.

₪

While the confusion, panic, and death unfolded on the plains below, the lions were safely perched above on various mountain ledges. They watched with a sense of detachment. Somehow, the situation below confirmed again the natural order of things. Lions were atop the animal kingdom. It was really no more or no less a fact of animal existence. If the herds had followed the rule of King, perhaps this would not have happened.

The pride had experienced intense discussions since the flooding had begun. Lionheart and a band of lions argued to extend help to bring those animals they could to higher ground. The will of the pride, led by the strong will of King, had kept them at bay. As he watched the disaster below, Lionheart told the group he could no longer sit by and watch the carnage without helping the dwellers to higher ground.

King told him to go and help the dwellers if he chose and that he could take with him all those who wanted to follow. King thought to himself, *this is an excellent opportunity to get rid of my irritating brother permanently—and all of those who are sympathetic with his cause!* When Lionheart led a band of lions down the mountain in a rescue attempt, King assembled a band of his own to destroy the trail permanently. He had in mind a plan that would work to perfection!

There was a sizeable reservoir lake at the higher elevation that served as an alternative source of water for the lions. It also fed a hidden oasis on the other side of the mountain that contained luscious grasslands, meadows, and beautiful foliage. It resembled Utopia of old, before the crisis began. The lake had been dammed by the lions to control the flow of water as needed. King's plan was to allow Lionheart and his band of "bleeding-hearts" to descend the mountain and then flood the trail. The intent was to wash them and the dwellers they saved back into the torrent of the flood that had reached proportions that none of them could survive. King was astounded at how the flood had appeared to take care of all their problems. When all was said and done, everything would be restored to the original Prideland. After all, they didn't really need the food supply of the herds below anyway. It was all so perfect!

₪

As the small band of lions made their way down the winding mountain trail, King and his band were busily making their way to the dammed reservoir.

At a turn in the trail, Lionheart's band came face to face with the herd band. The three herd leaders stepped forward as if ready to do battle with the lions. After all, there was only death below anyway.

Lionheart quickly told them they had come to help get the herds to safety. "Why would you help us?" shouted Zeb. "All you have done is attempted to control us. Now we will not be stopped even if it costs us our lives."

Lionheart simply stood his ground and listened. Finally, he said, "You have no reason to trust us. I can only tell you of our intent. We have risked our lives by leaving the pride to provide you assistance. That is all I can say."

Gazellong, being the most intuitive of the three herdleaders, stepped forward and said, "I believe him. We really have no choice. We have no idea where we are going, except up."

Carivan said to Lionheart, "What do you have in mind?"

"There is a mountain trail that splits off from this one that leads to the other side of the mountain. We can reach safety there. It's just a short distance ahead of us," Lionheart explained.

There was a loud burst high above the mountain, similar to the breakthrough that had occurred when the flood first started. Lionheart knew instantly what King had done. He shouted, "We must hurry if we are to survive!"

When the herd band realized that not only were their lives at stake, but also the lives of the lions, there was little hesitancy to follow Lionheart. They quickly followed the lions up the mountain pass. Just as they reached the split in the trails, which were highly banked on each side, the first trickle of water began flowing down the path. The four bands quickly switched trails as their members ran past. Lionheart roared, "We must hurry or we'll be washed away. This is only the beginning. Let's get to the other side of the mountain!" The herd leaders quickly followed Lionheart and the others as torrents of water began to rage along the well-worn mountain trail they had just ascended.

₪

Up above at the dammed lake, King and his followers had begun removing the restraints that held the waters of the swollen mountain lake. What they had not realized was *how* swollen the lake had become due to the weeks of rainfall. When they began removing the restraints to ensure they had a flow that would flood Lionheart, his band of "do-gooders," as well as the dwellers they might save, they removed too many. The torrent began in an uncontrolled manner. The remaining restraints were washed away like twigs, and the entire

front of the mountainside became an unrestrained flood. King and his band were swept away in an instant down the mountain and into the raging waters on the plains below.

Nature took its course down the fall line to exactly the ledges where the lion bands were perched. Hearing the explosion, they barely had time to look up before being washed away like King and his band. The front of the mountain became a magnificent waterfall until the mountain lake once again reached its original level.

₪

The mixed band of lions, zebras, caribous, and gazelles led by Lionheart, Zeb, Carivan, and Gazellong, quickly made their way to the other side of the mountain. The winding trail finally gave way to a magnificent meadow where animals of all types were grazing. It looked much like a mixed plains herd, except there were more zebras and fewer gazelles. Zeb thought to himself, *so this explains the disappearance of zebras from our herd.*

There were also a number of crossbred herds, since they had lived together in this meadow for some time. The banded herd was still astounded by the oasis of mixed herd animals and continued to stare at them as if observing strangers—rather than kin. Lionheart embarrassingly explained that this herd was a secret food

source of the lions in the event starvation occurred on the plains.

Lionheart said, "I know it means little to your herds to say we are sorry, but my band had never agreed to or accepted my brother's plan. In fact, our views created strong dissension within our Lair. When the flooding began, we decided we could no longer ignore the incredible loss of life. When we decided to help your band, we knew we could never return to the pride."

Zeb stepped forward and thanked Lionheart and his band for saving their lives. Just then, as if Earth Mother had been waiting for confirmation of Her key to balance, the rains abruptly stopped. As the clouds flowed by, clearing could be seen off to the north—where the rains had originated that brought the devastation to the plains.

It was not by accident that such clearing abruptly occurred. It was their unwitting achievement of the "key to balance" of the ecosystem. The key began falling into place when the three leaders of the various herds joined together out of survival, ensured by Earth Mother's intervention at certain critical times. *The key to balance was the commitment of each of the animal groups to live compatibly with each other within nature's broad design*; in essence, an intricate system of relationships among the four animal groups based upon trust, equality, and unity (see page 80), where no animal group was considered to be superior to the others. Compatibility occurred among the new leaders of Utopia

when domination, control, and power were replaced with cooperation, collaboration, and unity. They vowed that survival would be unnecessary as a motivation for their future cooperation. They all agreed that they had learned the lesson of resolving differences by a huge loss of life—and jointly promised that such a lesson would never have to be learned again. As legend was passed to subsequent generations, balance was eventually restored to the plains of Utopia, and it appeared *again*, that they would *live happily ever after!*

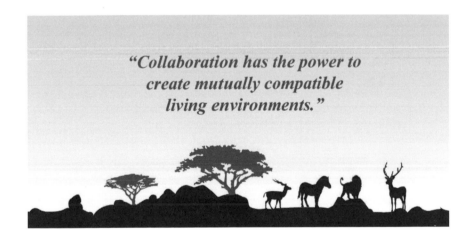

*"Collaboration has the power to create mutually compatible living environments."*

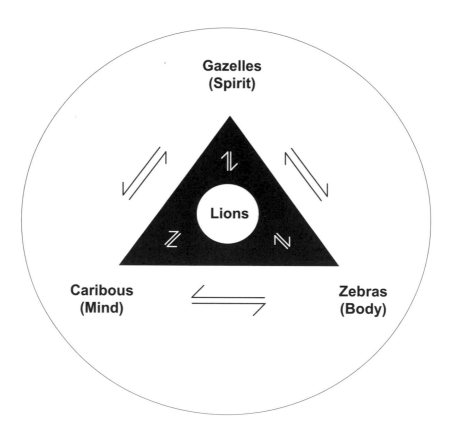

**The key to balance** – An intricate system of relationships of each animal group with the others based upon trust, equality, and unity. As described in italics in each chapter, the graphic represents body (zebras), mind (caribous), and spirit (gazelles) driven by the leadership of the lions. The model implies that inner balance of body, mind, and spirit is a reflection of the outer balance of the ecosystem.

William A. Guillory, Ph.D.

## The Aftermath

*M*any years after The Great Flood, the fable was still being told to subsequent generations of the three brave warriors who were led by a young female zebra to safety from the devastating floodwaters. The fable tells how a daring band of lions had led the band of zebras, caribous, and gazelles to a mountain oasis to establish a united Utopia. Even the lions had become part of the united partnership by providing the leadership that was critical to ensuring a bountiful environment. They discovered that they were all an interconnected part of the key to balance.

₪

The waters receded in time, and Earth Mother took full charge of the restoration process. She meticulously blended the ingredients, in Her own time frame, to produce a plain of flora unlike any ever seen before on Earth. It was a masterpiece. When She was complete, She brought the animals down from their mountain oasis to again populate the magnificent plains. She wondered, *what would they do this time? Had they learned the essential lessons of compatible living? Would separation, polarization, and domination of each other emerge again?* And, most of all, She wondered, *how many times do I have to run this experiment before giving up?*

## The Seven Principles of Cultural Compatibility

Listed below are the seven principles necessary to create culturally compatible living environments. Each of these principles has been sequentially developed in each of the seven chapters of this book.

1) **Inclusion**—sharing power and decision making to create a society (or planet) of equals

2) **Integration**—transcending one's group identification to become part of a greater whole; to create true unity

3) **Respect**—realizing that acceptance by others begins with the unconditional acceptance of yourself

4) **Transformation**—the invalidation of ethnocentric beliefs to create an acceptance of differences

5) **Empathy**—seeing through the eyes of others as the basis for reconciling conflicting differences

6) **Cooperation**—working together as equal partners to create solutions that are mutually beneficial

7) **Collaboration**—sharing risks and consequences to create mutually supportive living environments

 **A**nimal **K**ingdom

## Animal Kingdom Discussion Questions

1. Did you make associations of the animal groups with various societal groups?

2. What do you consider the major issue the Lions were dealing with in relationship to the other animal groups?

3. What do you consider the major issue the Zebras were dealing with within their own animal group?

4. What is the major issue the Caribous were confronting within their own animal group?

5. What is the major issue the Gazelles were dealing with as it relates to resolving the food supply shortage?

6. In terms of cultural compatibility, do you believe addressing the concerns of all is more productive than individual social Darwinism? Why?

7. What is the major belief or value that keeps groups separate and polarized? Why?

8. Do you believe dissension and division between (and among) groups will eventually lead to system breakdown? If yes, give an example to support your opinion.

9. Do you believe most organizations are truly committed to diversity, by results? Give an example to support your opinion.

10. Do you believe that diversity has the potential to develop the human technology necessary to create a culturally compatible planet? Explain why.

# About the Author

**William A. Guillory, Ph.D.** is the CEO and founder of Innovations Consulting International, Inc. He has presented more than 4,000 seminars throughout corporate America, Europe, Asia Pacific, Mexico, and Canada. He has facilitated seminars for over 300 corporations, including the senior management of American Airlines, Avon Products, Inc., Eastman Kodak Company, Electronic Data Systems, Lockheed Martin Corporation, Sandia National Laboratories, Rohm and Haas Company, Texas Instruments, Sempra Energy, DaimlerChrysler, Kellogg Corporation, and many other Fortune 500 corporations.

Dr. Guillory is an authority on diversity, empowerment, leadership, creativity, and work-life quality and balance. He is a widely requested and popular conference and keynote speaker on these subjects as well as spirituality in the workplace. He is the author of four books on personal transformation, *"Realizations," "It's All an Illusion," "Destined to Succeed,"* and *"The Guides,"* and is the co-author of the management book titled *"EMPOWERMENT For High Performing Organizations."* His most recent books are "The Living Organization – *Spirituality in the Workplace,"* and *"Animal Kingdom – A Diversity Fable."*

Prior to establishing Innovations, Dr. Guillory was a physical chemist of international renown. His distinguished awards and appointments include an Alfred P. Sloan Fellowship, an Alexander von Humboldt appointment at the University of Frankfurt, a Ralph Metcalf Chair at Marquette University, and the Chancellor's Distinguished Lectureship at the University of California at Berkeley. Dr. Guillory founded Innovations in 1985 following a period of intense personal growth which led to a career change to individual and organization transformation.

 **A**nimal **K**ingdom

# Innovations International, Inc.

Innovations is a global human resource development corporation specializing in personal and organizational transformation. We exist to assist organizations in achieving their business performance goals while maintaining their personal and collective well-being.

Our specializations in consulting include:

- Diversity
- Empowerment
- Leadership
- Creativity and Innovation

- Work-Life Integration
- High-Performance Organizations
- Spirituality in the Workplace

Our most recent offering is *The FuturePerfect Organization – Driven by Quantum Leadership.*

These specializations include comprehensive programs involving consulting, seminars, audits and assessments, coaching, strategic planning, and interactive multimedia learning.

Our multimedia and online series in Diversity and High Performance feature CD-ROM interactive processes including video presentations and scenarios, question-and-answer discussions, interactive case studies, and self-management skills.

For information regarding Innovations' programs, telephone, write, fax, email, or visit our web page:

**Innovations International, Inc.**
310 East 4500 South, Suite 420
Salt Lake City, UT 84107 USA
Tel: (801) 268-3313 ◆ Fax: (801) 268-3422
Email: innovationsintl@qwest.net ◆ Web site: www.innovint.com

## Other Titles by William A. Guillory

*Realizations*

*The Business of Diversity*

*The Global Manager*

*It's All an Illusion*

*EMPOWERMENT*
*for High-Performing*
*Organizations*

*Destined to Succeed*

*The Guides*

*Rodney – The Children's Series*

*Rodney Goes to the Country – The Children's Series*

*The Living Organization –*
*Spirituality in the Workplace*

*Living Without Fear*

*Tick Tock!...Who Broke the Clock?*

*The FuturePerfect Organization –*
*Driven by Quantum Leadership*

*The Roadmap to Diversity,*
*Inclusion, and High Performance*